Ladybird Read

It Is Friday!

Inspired by
The Very Hungry Caterpillar
by Eric Carle

4

What day is it today?

It is Monday!

It is Tuesday.

It is Wednesday!

It is Thursday.

It is Friday!

It is Saturday.

It is Sunday!

Your turn!

1 **Listen. Color in the words.**

1
| Monday | Wednesday |

2
| Saturday | Sunday |

3
| Friday | Monday |

4
| Tuesday | Thursday |

2 **Listen. Put a** ✓ **by the correct words.**

1 a It is Monday.

b It is Friday.

2 a It is Saturday.

b It is Wednesday.

3 a It is Tuesday.

b It is Thursday.

4 a It is Monday.

b It is Friday.

15

3 Read and clap!

It is Monday. Hooray!

It is Tuesday. Hooray!

It is Wednesday. Hooray!

It is Thursday. Hooray!

It is Friday. Hooray!

It is Saturday. Hooray!

It is Sunday. Hooray!

What day is it today?